Good Ol' Noah Had an Ark

E-I-E-I-O

Written by Martha Bolton • Illustrated by Lyn Boyer Nelles

Zonderkidz ™

The Children's Group of ZondervanPublishingHouse

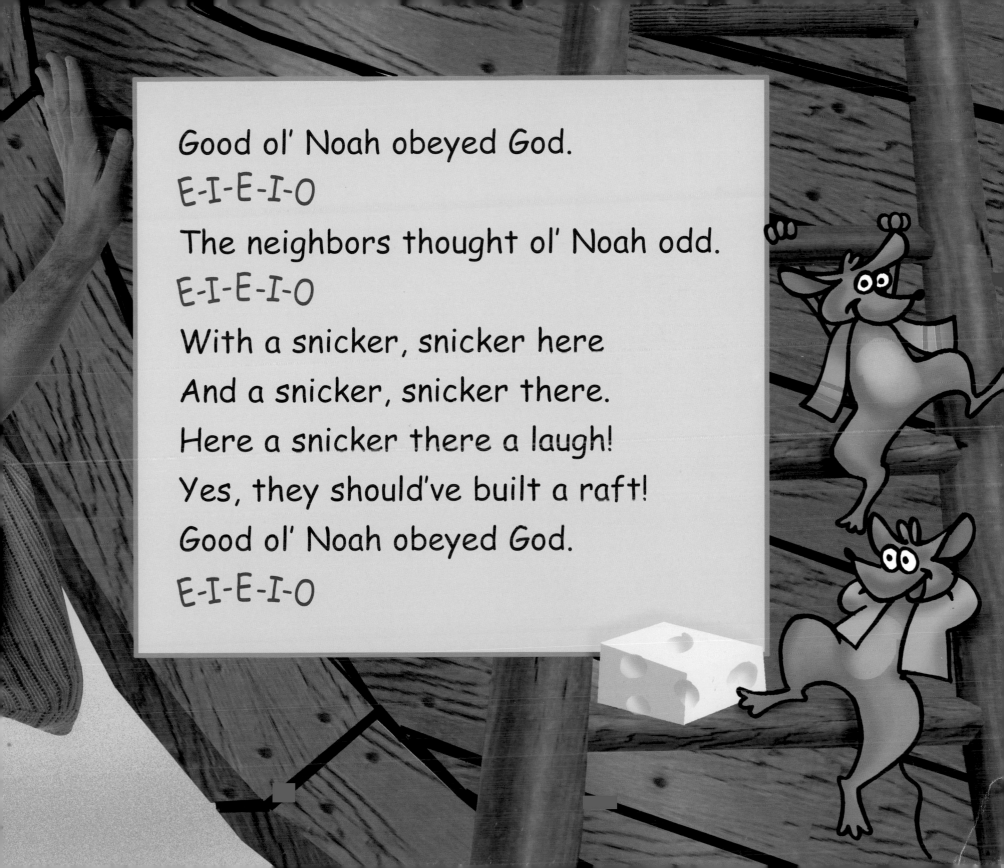

Good ol' Noah obeyed God.
E-I-E-I-O
The neighbors thought ol' Noah odd.
E-I-E-I-O
With a snicker, snicker here
And a snicker, snicker there.
Here a snicker there a laugh!
Yes, they should've built a raft!
Good ol' Noah obeyed God.
E-I-E-I-O

Good ol' Noah built an ark.

E-I-E-I-O

He pounded nails from dawn till dark.

E-I-E-I-O

With an "Ouch! Ouch!" here

And an "Ouch! Ouch!" there.

Here an "Ouch!" there an "Ouch!"

No wonder he was such a grouch!

Good ol' Noah built an ark.

E-I-E-I-O

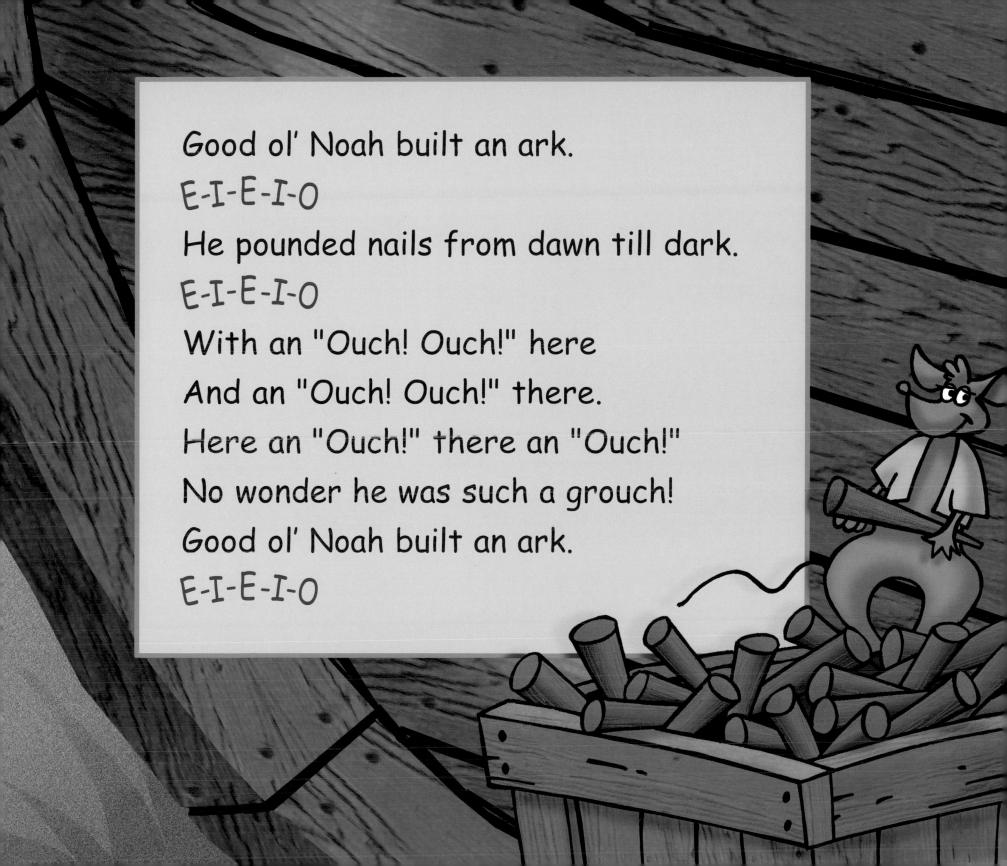

Good ol' Noah had an ark.
E-I-E-I-O
And on that ark were two giraffes.
E-I-E-I-O
With a neck stretched here
And a neck stretched there.
Here a neck, there a neck,
Noah chased 'em 'round the deck!
Good ol' Noah had an ark.
E-I-E-I-O

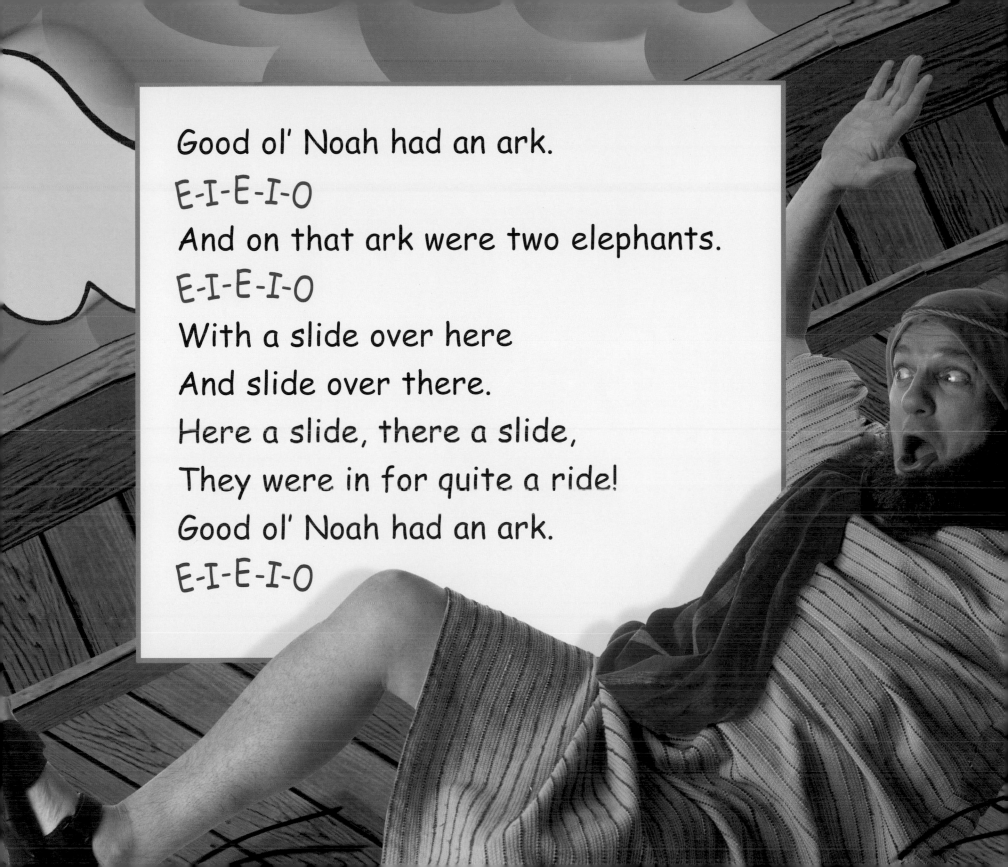

Good ol' Noah had an ark.

E-I-E-I-O

And on that ark were two snuggly bears.

E-I-E-I-O

With a bear hug here

And a bear hug there.

Here a hug, there a squeeze,

With those bears he'd never freeze!

Good ol' Noah had an ark.

E-I-E-I-O

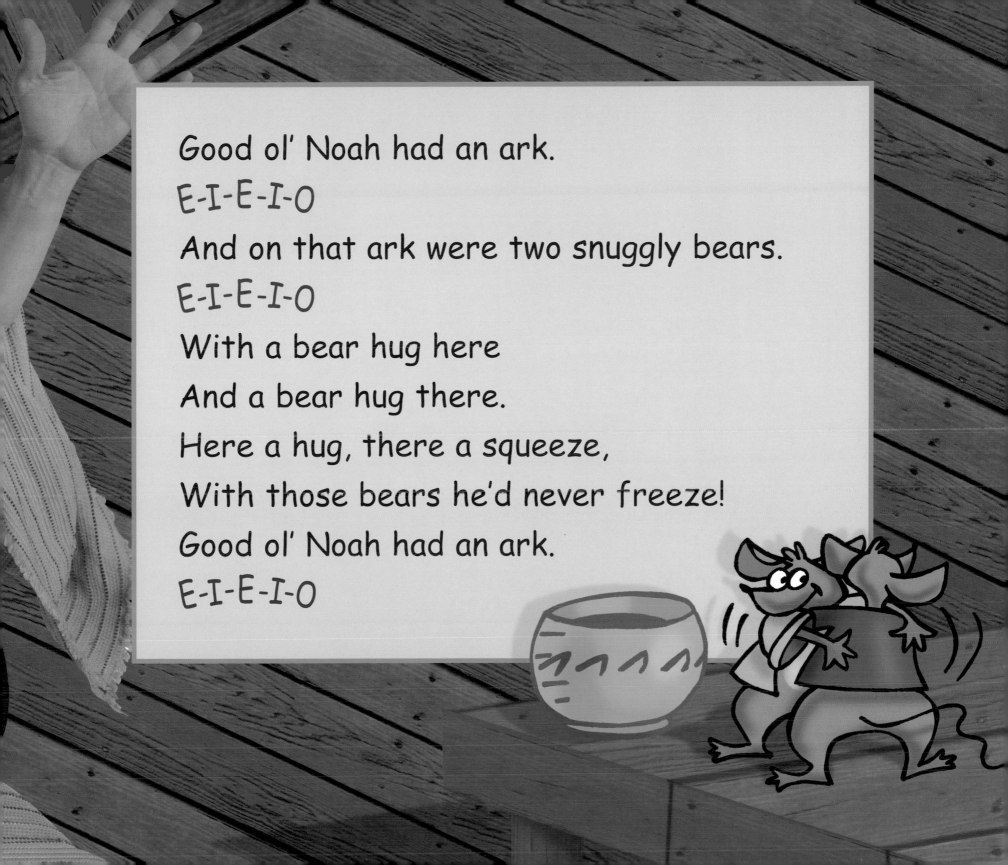

Good ol' Noah had an ark.
E-I-E-I-O
And on that ark were two
hip bunnies.
E-I-E-I-O
With a hip, hop here
And a hip, hop there.
Here a hip, there a hop,
Hippin', hoppin' with no stoppin'!
Good ol' Noah had an ark.
E-I-E-I-O

Good ol' Noah had an ark.

E-I-E-I-O

And on that ark were two chunky chickens

E-I-E-I-O

With an egg roll here, and an egg roll there,

Here an egg, there an egg,

Rollin' between ol' Noah's legs!

Good ol' Noah had an ark.

E-I-E-I-O

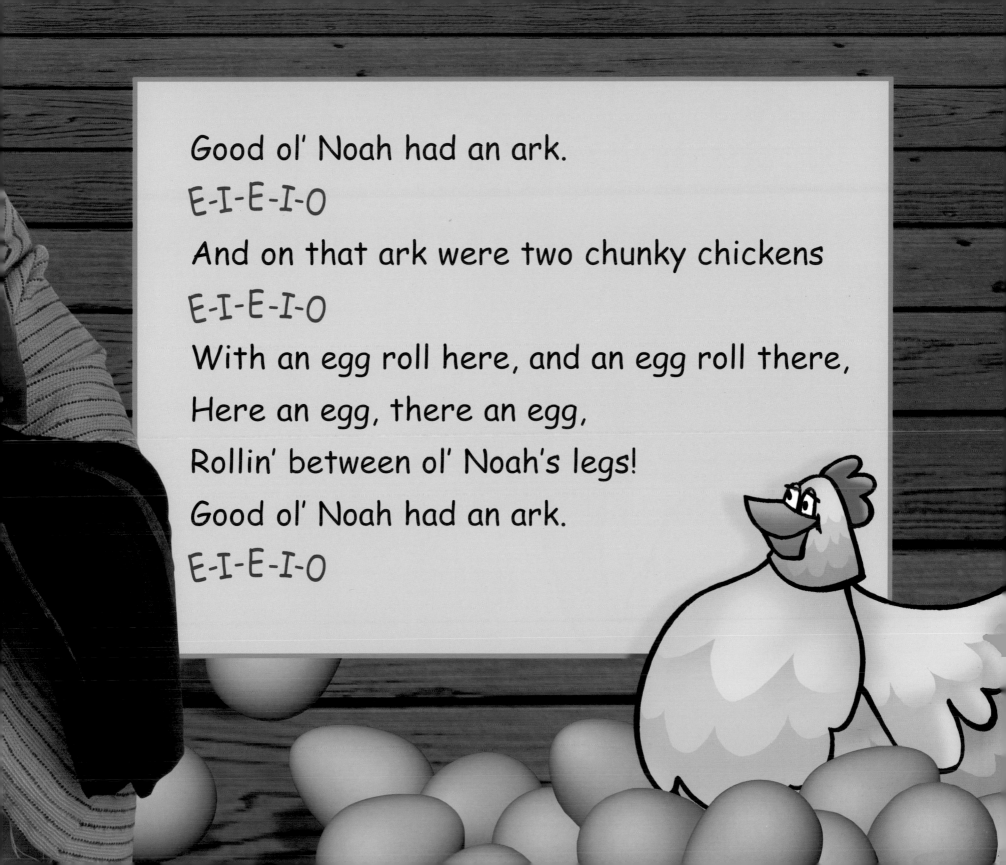

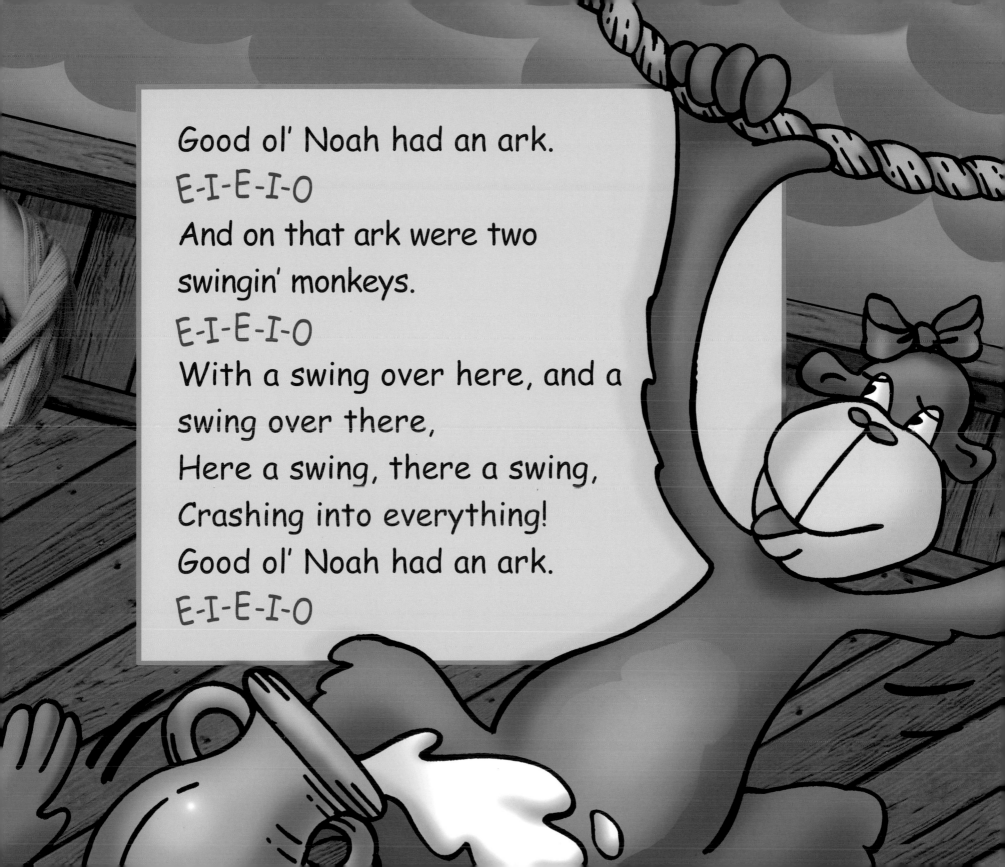

Good ol' Noah had an ark.
E-I-E-I-O
And on that ark were two swingin' monkeys.
E-I-E-I-O
With a swing over here, and a swing over there,
Here a swing, there a swing,
Crashing into everything!
Good ol' Noah had an ark.
E-I-E-I-O

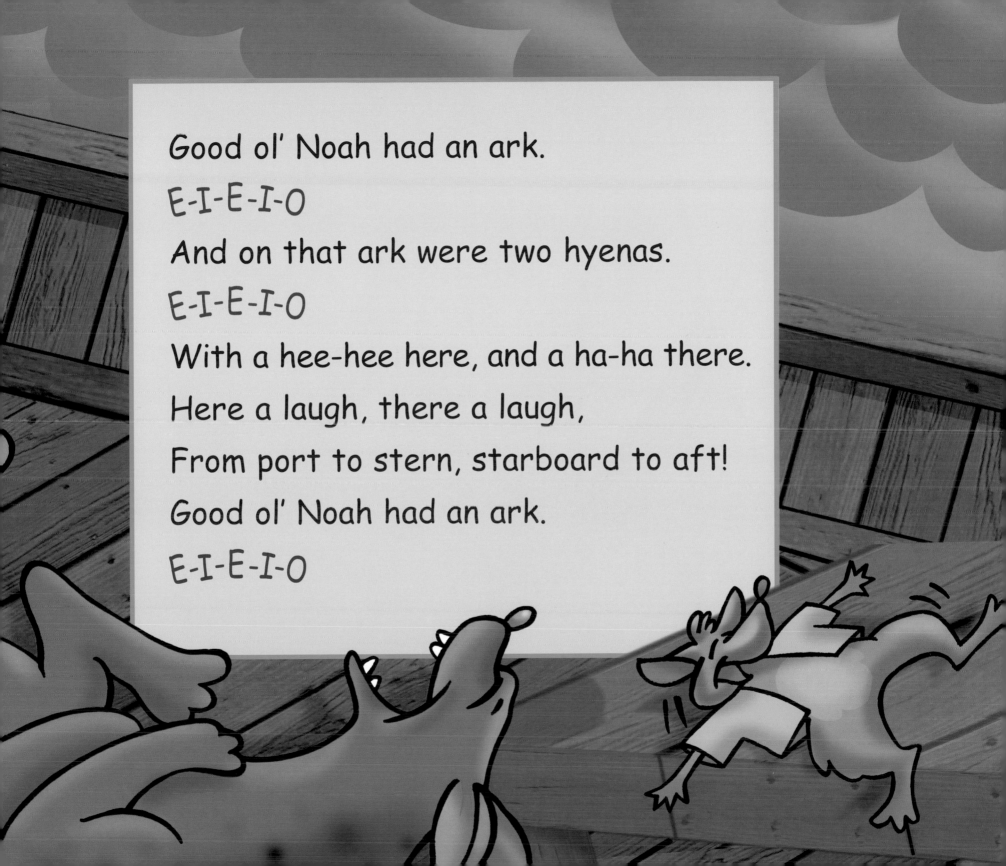

Good ol' Noah had an ark.

E-I-E-I-O

And on that ark were two hyenas.

E-I-E-I-O

With a hee-hee here, and a ha-ha there.

Here a laugh, there a laugh,

From port to stern, starboard to aft!

Good ol' Noah had an ark.

E-I-E-I-O

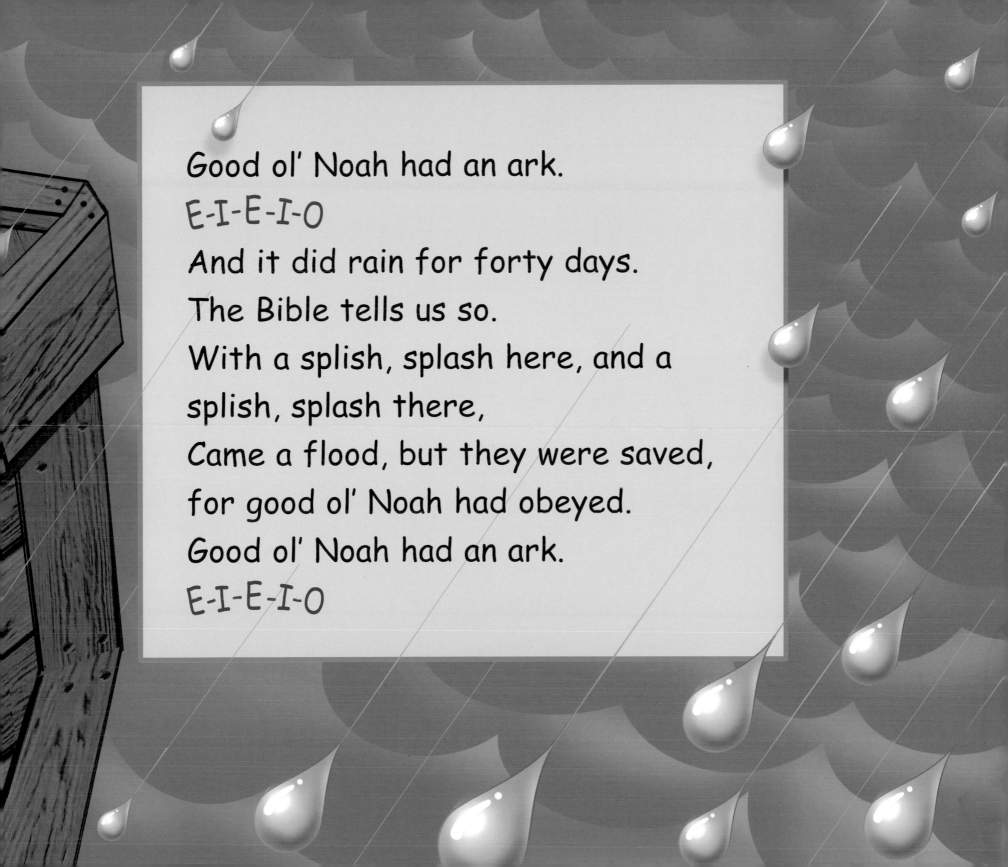

Good ol' Noah had an ark.

E-I-E-I-O

And it did rain for forty days.

The Bible tells us so.

With a splish, splash here, and a

splish, splash there,

Came a flood, but they were saved,

for good ol' Noah had obeyed.

Good ol' Noah had an ark.

E-I-E-I-O

Martha Bolton spent over fifteen years as a staff writer for Bob Hope and has also written for Phyllis Diller, Bill Gaither, and others. The author of twenty-nine books, she pens the popular Cafeteria Lady column for *Brio* magazine. Martha is the mother of three sons and lives in Nashville, TN.

Lyn Boyer Nelles has been an illustrator for 20 years. Her clients include *Reader's Digest* and The Book of the Month Club. Lyn, her husband, and their two children live in Williamsburg, Michigan.

Good Ol' Noah Had An Ark, E-I-E-I-O
Text copyright © 2000 by Mark Lowry and Martha Bolton
Illustrations copyright © 2000 by Lyn Boyer Nelles
Photography copyright © 2000 by Russ Harrington
Requests for information should be addressed to:

Zonderkidz™

The Children's Group of ZondervanPublishingHouse
Grand Rapids, Michigan 49530
www.zonderkidz.com

Zonderkidz is a trademark of The Zondervan Corporation

ISBN: 0-310-23198-1

Art Direction by Jody Langley
Design by Michelle Lenger

Printed in China

00 01 02 03 04 05 /HK/ 10 9 8 7 6 5 4 3 2 1